Let's Make Your Clock!

How It Works

- Cut along the gray line. Start from here ✂.
- Put the clock hands on the face. Use a pin to help keep them in place, or just move them gently.
- Decorate. You can draw on the clock face and hands to add your own style!
- You can use this clock to help you when doing the activities in this book.

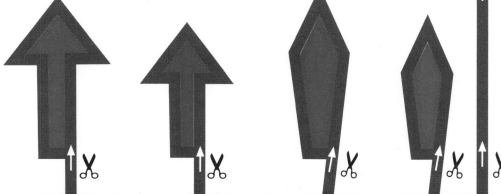

**Everyday Math
Telling Time**

Table of Contents

KUM⊙N

Write the time shown on the clock.

1.

(1 :00)

2.

(:00)

3.

(:)

4.

(:)

5.

(:)

6.

(:)

7.

(:)

8.

(:)

9.

(:)

10.

(:)

11.

(:)

12.

(:)

5

Draw the hands on each clock to show the time.

1. 1 :00

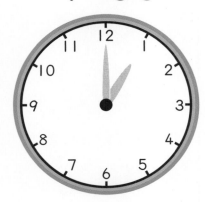

2. 4 :00

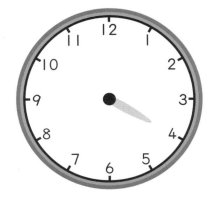

3. 8 :00

4. 11 :00

5. 2 :00

6. 9 :00

7. 3:00

8. 6:00

9. 12:00

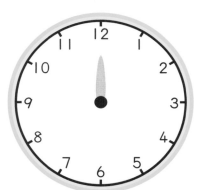

10. 5:00

11. 7:00

12. 10:00

3 Choose the correct time.

1.

☐ 8:00

☑ 9:00

☐ 10:00

2.

☐ 4:00

☐ 5:00

☐ 6:00

3.

☐ 5:00

☐ 6:00

☐ 7:00

Did you know "two o'clock" is the same time as "2:00"?

4.

☐ It's two o'clock.

☐ It's three o'clock.

☑ It's four o'clock.

5.

☐ It's one o'clock.

☐ It's three o'clock.

☐ It's five o'clock.

6.

☐ It's ten o'clock.

☐ It's eleven o'clock.

☐ It's twelve o'clock.

4

Match the clocks that show the same time.

1.

2.

3.

Remember, when both hands point to the same number, the long hand covers the short hand.

4.

5.

6.

11

Write the time Anna does each activity.

Being able to tell time can help you be ready for daily activities!

I read at __10:00__ .

I play soccer at ____:____ .

I play the guitar at ____:____ .

13

6 Draw the hands on the clocks to show the time Brooklyn does each activity.

I have breakfast at 8:00.

I play the piano at 12:00.

I wash the dishes at 7:00.

15

Write the time shown on the clock.

1.

(3 :30)

2.

(:30)

3.

(:   )

4.

(:   )

5.

(:   )

6.

(:   )

When the time is written ":30" it is 30 minutes past the hour. Notice that the hour hand moves a little bit too. It is halfway between this hour and the next hour.

7.

(:   )

8.

(:   )

9.

(:   )

10.

(:   )

11.

(:   )

12.

(:   )

Draw the hands on each clock to show the time.

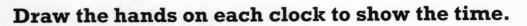

1.   4 : 30

2.   6 : 30

3.   10 : 30

4.   8 : 30

5.   2 : 30

6.   7 : 30

Do you know the trick to telling half hours? The long hand will always be on the 6!

7. 3 : 30

8. 1 : 30

9. 11 : 30

10. 12 : 30

11. 5 : 30

12. 9 : 30

19

Choose the correct time.

1.

☐ 7:30

☐ 8:30

☐ 9:30

2.

☐ 3:30

☐ 4:30

☐ 5:30

3.

☐ 10:30

☐ 11:30

☐ 12:30

4.

☐ It's two thirty.

☐ It's three thirty.

☐ It's four thirty.

5.

☐ It's half past five.

☐ It's half past six.

☐ It's half past seven.

6.

☐ It's ten o'clock.

☐ It's half past ten.

☐ It's eleven thirty.

10

Match the clocks that show the same time.

1.

 •

 •

•
10:30

•
2:30

2.

 •

 •

•
4 30

•
11 30

3.

 •

 •

•
8:30

•
5:30

Need help matching the times on the clocks? Try looking for the number the short hand is pointing to on the opposite clock face.

4.

●   ●

●   ●

5.

●   ●

●   ●

6.

●   ●

●   ●

23

11 **Write the time Charlotte does each activity.**

I draw a cartoon at _____ : _____ .

I eat a snack at _____ : _____ .

I dance at _____ : _____ .

25

12 Draw the hands on the clocks to show the time David does each activity.

I play with my sister at 11:30.

I go to the park at 1:30.

I play basketball at 5:30.

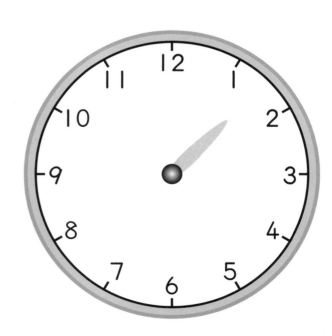

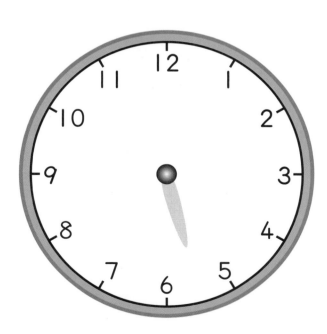

27

Write the time shown on the clock.

1.

(2 : 15)

2.

(: 15)

3.

(:   )

4.

(:   )

5.

(:   )

6.

(:   )

7.

(2 : 45)

8.

(:)

9.

(:)

10.

(:)

11.

(:)

12.

(:)

29

Draw the hands on each clock to show the time.

1. 5:15

2. 10:15

3. 1:15

4. 12:15

5. 8:15

6. 2:15

When the long hand points to the 3, it is 15 minutes past the hour or ":15." When the long hand points to the 9, it is 45 minutes past the hour or ":45."

7. 1:45

8. 7:45

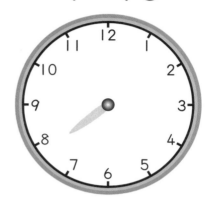

9. 11:45

10. 6:45

11. 9:45

12. 4:45

Choose the correct time.

1.

- ☐ 6:15
- ☐ 6:45
- ☐ 7:15

2.

- ☐ 2:45
- ☐ 3:15
- ☐ 3:45

3.

- ☐ 9:15
- ☐ 9:45
- ☐ 10:45

Saying "a quarter to" is another way to say "15 minutes until a new hour." For example, "a quarter to 2" means it is 1:45.

4.

☐ It's one fifteen.

☐ It's one thirty.

☐ It's two fifteen.

5.

☐ It's a quarter to four.

☐ It's a quarter to five.

☐ It's a quarter to six.

6.

☐ It's a quarter to ten.

☐ It's a quarter to eleven.

☐ It's a quarter past eleven.

16 Match the clocks that show the same time.

1.  •   •
2:15

 •   • 5:15

2.  •   •
10:45

 •   •
7:45

3.  •   •
9:15

 •   •
6:15

Need help matching the times on the clocks? Try looking for the number the short hand is pointing to on the opposite clock face.

4.

8 : 45

•

•

•

•

3 : 45

5.

1 15

•

•

•

•

11 45

6.

4 : 45

•

•

12 : 15

•

•

35

Write the time Eva does each activity.

I jump rope at _____ : _____.

I watch a movie at _____ : _____.

I read a book at _____ : _____.

37

Draw the hands on the clocks to show the time Frankie does each activity.

I water the plants at 4:45.

I do a puzzle at 12:15.

I listen to music at 11:45.

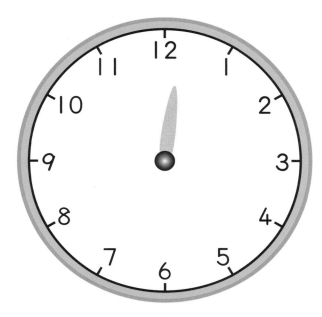

Write the time shown on the clock.

1.

(8 :05)

2.

(6 :10)

3.

(:   )

4.

(:   )

5.

(:   )

6.

(:   )

Let's learn to tell time in five-minute jumps.

7.

(:   )

8.

(:   )

9.

(:   )

10.

(:   )

11.

(:   )

12.

(:   )

41

Draw the hands on each clock to show the time.

1. 6:20

2. 4:25

3. 2:35

4. 7:40

5. 10:50

6. 8:10

7. 12:05

8. 5:35

9. 9:10

10. 3:20

11. 1:25

12. 11:40

Choose the correct time.

1.

- [ ] 8 : 05
- [ ] 8 : 10
- [ ] 8 : 15

2.

- [ ] 10 : 20
- [ ] 11 : 20
- [ ] 11 : 25

3.

- [ ] 2 : 50
- [ ] 3 : 40
- [ ] 3 : 50

4.

☐ It's three oh five.

☐ It's three ten.

☐ It's three fifteen.

3:05

5.

☐ It's five ten.

☐ It's five twenty.

☐ It's five twenty-five.

5:20

6.

☐ It's eleven fifteen.

☐ It's a quarter to twelve.

☐ It's eleven fifty-five.

11:55

22

Match the clocks that show the same time.

1.

 • •

• •

2.

 • •

 • •

3.

 • •

 • •

Need help matching the times on the clocks? Try looking for the number the short hand is pointing to on the opposite clock face.

4.

7:55

10:05

5.

9:10

1:50

6.

2:40

11:20

Write the time Grace does each activity.

Can you think of what time you do your favorite activity?

I bake cookies at _____ : _____ .

I skateboard at _____ : _____ .

I write a story at _____ : _____ .

24

Draw the hands on the clocks to show the time Hector does each activity.

I visit the library at 4:35.

I eat ice cream at 2:50.

I go to the supermarket at 5:05.

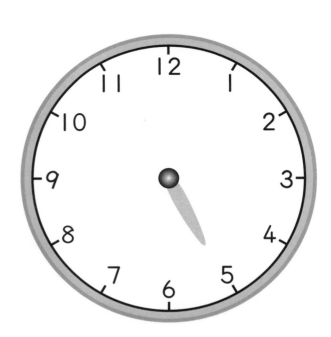

Did you draw each clock correctly?
Give yourself a pat on the back!

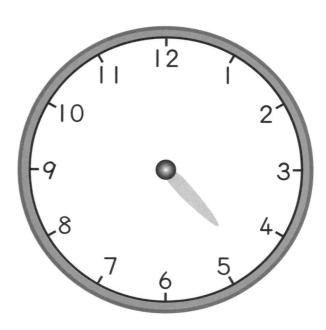

25 Write the time shown on the clock.

1.

(3 : 01)

2.

(4 : 02)

3.

(:)

4.

(:)

5.

(:)

6.

(:)

7.

(:   )

8.

(:   )

9.

(:   )

10.

(:   )

11.

(:   )

12.

(:   )

Draw the hands on each clock to show the time.

1. 1:01

2. 4:06

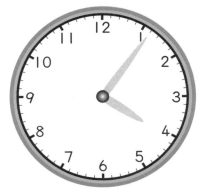

3. 8:09

4. 11:22

5. 2:32

6. 9:46

7. 3:47

8. 6:33

9. 12:34

10. 5:09

11. 7:19

12. 10:21

27 Choose the correct time.

1.

- [ ] 8:12
- [ ] 8:14
- [ ] 8:16

2.

- [ ] 6:23
- [ ] 6:31
- [ ] 6:33

3.

- [ ] 5:41
- [ ] 5:43
- [ ] 5:39

4.

☐ It's four ten.

☐ It's four eleven.

☐ It's four twelve.

5.

☐ It's three forty-six.

☐ It's three fifty-six.

☐ It's a quarter to four.

6.

☐ It's ten fifty-five.

☐ It's ten fifty-nine.

☐ It's ten fifty-eight.

28

Match the clocks that show the same time.

1.  ● ●  8:44

 ● ●  8:33

2.  ● ●  10:06

 ● ●  10:36

3.  ● ●  9:18

 ● ●  9:48

Need help matching the times on the clocks? Try looking for the number the long hand is pointing to on the opposite clock face.

4.

7:51

7:53

5.

5:22

5:24

6.

1:16

1:19

59

Write the time Isaac does each activity.

I paint at _____ : _____ .

I make a sandwich at _____ : _____ .

I practice the flute at _____ : _____ .

61

30

Draw the hands on the clocks to show the time Jerome does each activity.

I feed my cat at 6:04.

I do stretches at 3:47.

I ride the bus at 7:26.

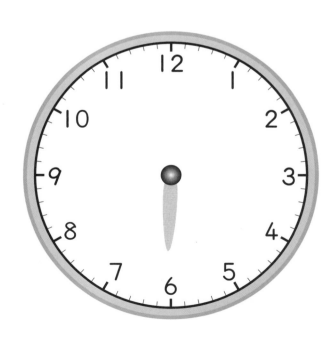

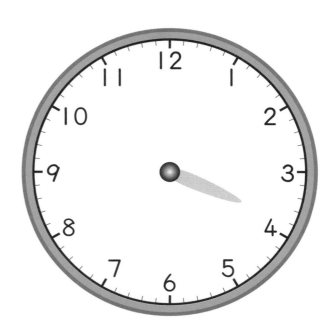

When does each activity happen: a.m. or p.m.?

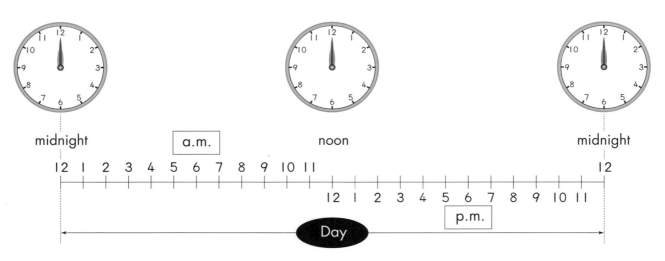

midnight   a.m.   noon   midnight

12 1 2 3 4 5 6 7 8 9 10 11   12 1 2 3 4 5 6 7 8 9 10 11

p.m.

Day

Sunrise

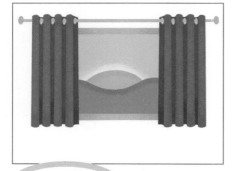

(6 a.m.) / 6 p.m.

Breakfast

7 a.m. / 7 p.m.

Dinner

7 a.m. / 7 p.m.

Play outside

1 a.m. / 1 p.m.

64

A clock only shows 12 hours, but there are 24 hours in a day. A.m. and p.m. are used to tell the difference between the time during the day and at night.

Walk the dog

4 a.m. / 4 p.m.

After school

3 a.m. / 3 p.m.

Go to bed

9 a.m. / 9 p.m.

Math class

10 a.m. / 10 p.m.

Lunch

12 a.m. / 12 p.m.

Moon in the sky

12 a.m. / 12 p.m.

Draw the hands on each clock to show what time it will be.

1.

 I hour later

2.

 I hour later

3.

 I hour later

4.

I hour later

5.

I hour later

6.

I hour later

Write the time it will be.

1.

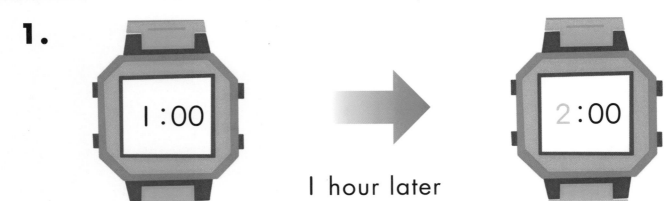

1:00 → 2:00

I hour later

2.

2:00 → 3:00

I hour later

3.

5:00 → :

I hour later

68

4.

I hour later

5.

I hour later

6.

I hour later

34 Draw a line to the clock that shows what time it will be.

1. Current time   I hour later

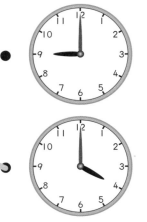

2. Current time   I hour later

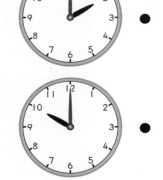

3. Current time   I hour later

Did you answer all of the questions correctly? Great job!

4. Current time

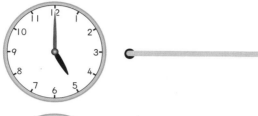

I hour later

6:00

8:00

5. Current time

I hour later

7:00

3:00

6. Current time

I hour later

2:00

11:00

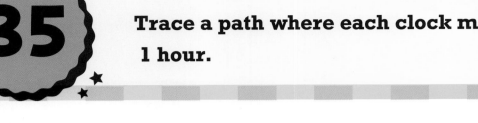

Trace a path where each clock moves forward 1 hour.

1.

2.

Each maze path shows clocks that move forward by one hour. Remember to look at the number the short hand is pointing to, or at the first number.

3.

Start

2:00	3:00	4:00	9:00
11:00	12:00	5:00	6:00
1:00	8:00	10:00	7:00

Goal

4.

Start

5:00	2:00	11:00	4:00
6:00	12:00	3:00	1:00
7:00	8:00	9:00	10:00

Goal

73

Draw the hands on the clocks to show the time Kennedy will do each activity.

 I will take a walk in 1 hour.

 I will play the violin in 1 hour.

 I will go to bed in 1 hour.

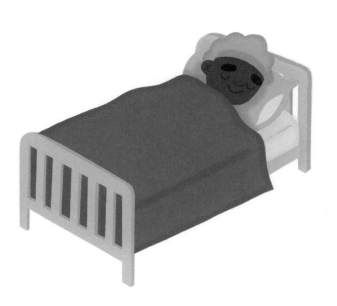

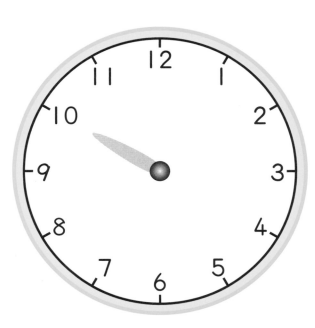

37

Write the time Liam will do each activity.

7:00   I will feed my dog in 1 hour.

9:00   I will study math in 1 hour.

5:00   I will come home in 1 hour.

8:00

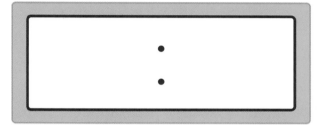

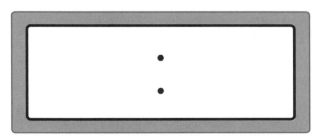

38

Draw the hands on each clock to show what time it will be.

1.

2 hours later

2.

3 hours later

3.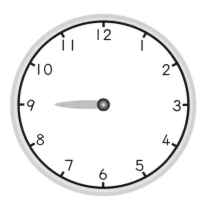

4 hours later

4.

5 hours later

5.

6 hours later

6.

7 hours later

39

Write the time it will be.

1.

5:00

2 hours later

7:00

2.

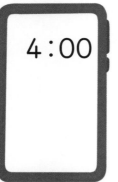

4:00

4 hours later

8:00

3.

1:00

5 hours later

:

Add the number of hours to get the new time!

4.

3:00 → :

6 hours later

5.

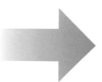

1:00 → :

7 hours later

6.

2:00 → :

3 hours later

40

Draw a line to the clock that shows what time it will be.

1. Current time   6 hours later

2. Current time   8 hours later

3. Current time   9 hours later

4. Current time   2 hours later

 •   •

 •   •

5. Current time   4 hours later

 •   •

 •   •

6. Current time   3 hours later

 •   •

 •   •

Trace a path where each clock moves forward by the number of hours shown.

1. 4 hours

Start

Goal

2. 5 hours

Start

Goal

3. 3 hours

Start

 12:00
 3:00
 4:00
 10:00

 1:00
 6:00
 5:00
 8:00

 7:00
 9:00
 12:00
 3:00

Goal

4. 2 hours

Start

 1 00
3 00
5 00
4 00

 6 00
8 00
7 00
9 00

 10 00
2 00
12 00
11 00

Goal

Draw the hands on the clocks to show the time Mason will do each activity.

 I will take a photo in 5 hours.

 I will help make dinner in 7 hours.

 I will go to the playground in 6 hours.

87

43

1 : 00	I will go swimming in 3 hours.
12 : 00	I will have science class in 2 hours.
4 : 00	I will have a slice of cake in 4 hours.

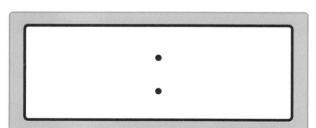

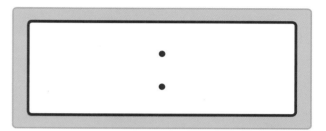

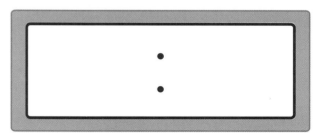

44

Draw the hands on each clock to show what time it will be.

1.

30 minutes later

2.

 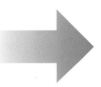 

30 minutes later

3.

30 minutes later

Practice writing what time it will be 30 minutes later. When the long hand moves 30 minute marks, it is the same as a half hour passing.

4.

30 minutes later

5.

30 minutes later

6.

30 minutes later

45

Write the time it will be.

1.

30 minutes later

2.

30 minutes later

3.

  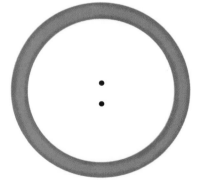

30 minutes later

4.

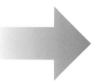

30 minutes later

5.

30 minutes later

6.

30 minutes later

93

46

Draw a line to the clock that shows what time it will be.

1.   Current time   30 minutes later

 ●   ●

 ●   ●

2.   Current time   30 minutes later

 ●   ●

 ●   ●

3.   Current time   30 minutes later

 ●   ●

 ●   ●

Did you match all of the clocks correctly? Great job!

4. Current time   30 minutes later

 •   •

 •   •

5. Current time   30 minutes later

 •   •

 •   •

6. Current time   30 minutes later

 •   •

 •   •

47

Trace a path where each clock moves forward 30 minutes.

1.

Start

Goal

2.

Start

Goal

Make sure each clock goes a half hour forward.

3.

Start

4:00 4:30 2:30 1:00

3:00 5:00 7:00 9:00

3:30 5:30 6:00 6:30

Goal

4.

Start

8:00 7:00 10:30 12:00

8:30 7:30 11:00 11:30

9:00 9:30

10:00 10:30

Goal

Draw the hands on the clocks to show the time Olivia will do each activity.

I will go to a birthday party in **30** minutes.

I will ride my bike in **30** minutes.

I will eat some fruit in **30** minutes.

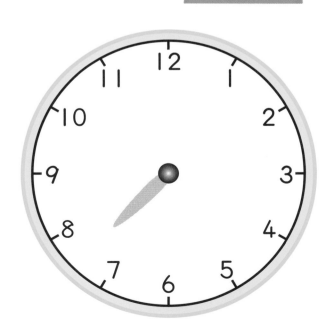

Olivia is having a busy day! What activities will you do today?

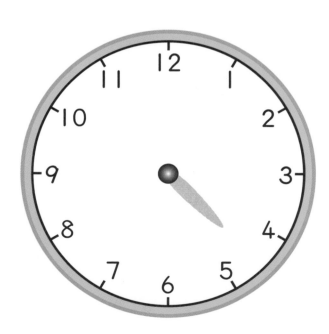

49

Write the time Parker will do each activity.

11:00   I will use the computer in 30 minutes.

12:00   I will go to the zoo in 30 minutes.

10:00   I will play volleyball in 30 minutes.

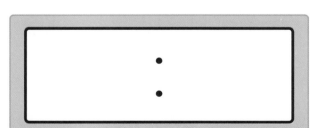

Did you answer the questions correctly? Great job!

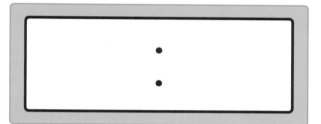

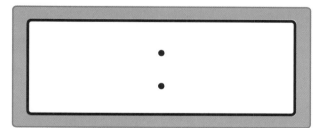

101

50

Draw the hands on each clock to show what time it will be.

1.

30 minutes later

2.

30 minutes later

3.

30 minutes later

4.

30 minutes later

5.

30 minutes later

6.

30 minutes later

Write the time it will be.

1.

30 minutes later

2.

30 minutes later

3.

30 minutes later

These questions keep getting harder! You should be proud of yourself for learning so much.

4.

 8 : 30   :

30 minutes later

5.

 6 : 30 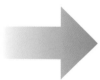  :

30 minutes later

6.

 7 : 30 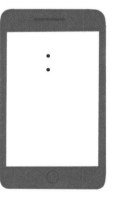 :

30 minutes later

52

Draw a line to the clock that shows what time it will be.

1. Current time

30 minutes later

2. Current time

30 minutes later

3. Current time

30 minutes later

106

4. Current time

 •

 •

30 minutes later

•

•

5. Current time

 •

 •

30 minutes later

•

•

6. Current time

 •

 •

30 minutes later

•

•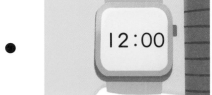

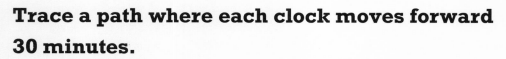

1.

Start

Goal

2.

Start

Goal

Remember to look at the hour and minutes on each clock.

3.

Start

 3:30  4:00  6:30  4:30

 5:00  4:30  7:00  5:00

 7:30  5:00  5:30  6:00

Goal

4.

Start

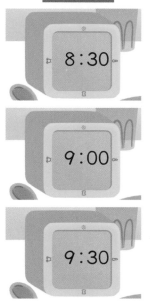 8:30 8:00 7:00 6:30

9:00 7:30 9:00 8:30

 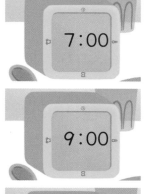 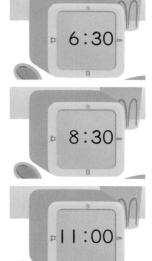

9:30 10:00  10:30 11:00

Goal

54

Draw the hands on the clocks to show the time Quinn will do each activity.

 I will eat pizza in 30 minutes.

 I will perform in a school play in 30 minutes.

 I will play the saxophone in 30 minutes.

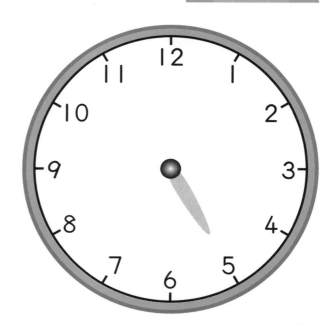

Did you answer all of the questions correctly? Great job!

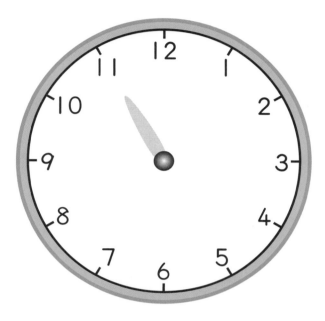

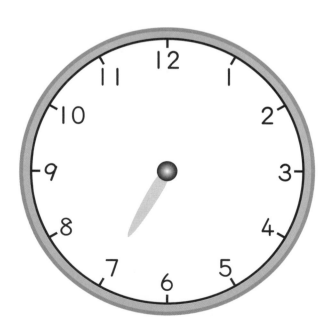

55

Write the time Riley will do each activity.

 9:30 I will practice the drums in 30 minutes.

11:30 I will play a board game in 30 minutes.

3:30 I will play with my brother in 30 minutes.

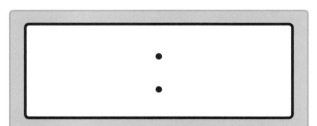

:

What will you do 30 minutes from now?

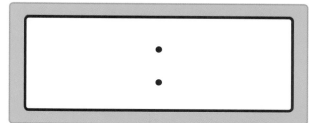

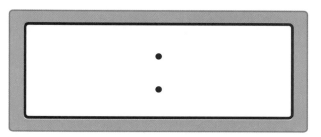

56

What time do Steve and Taylor do each activity?

1. Steve is going to the library in 2 hours. What time is it? What time will it be when he goes?

2. It takes Taylor 30 minutes to get to school. What time does she leave? What time does she arrive?

Answer Key

Everyday Math *Telling Time*

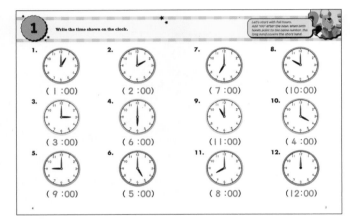

pages 4–5

Section 2 answers:
1. 1:00 2. 4:00 7. 3:00 8. 6:00
3. 8:00 4. 11:00 9. 12:00 10. 5:00
5. 2:00 6. 9:00 11. 7:00 12. 10:00

pages 6–7

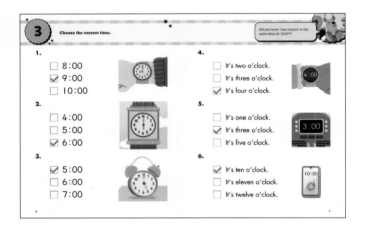

pages 8–9

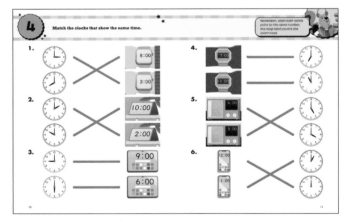

pages 10–11

116

pages 12–13

pages 14–15

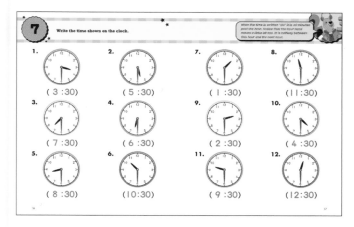

pages 16–17

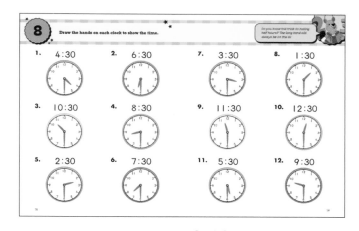

pages 18–19

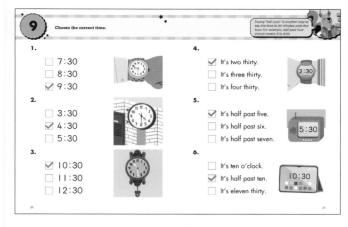

pages 20–21

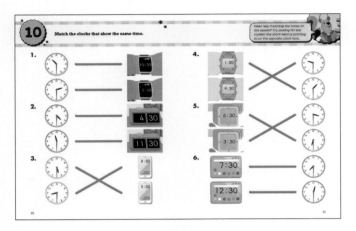

pages 22–23

pages 24–25

pages 26–27

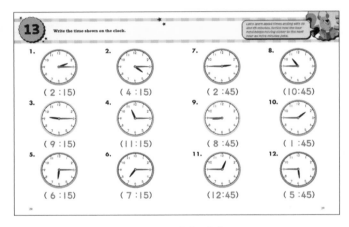

pages 28–29

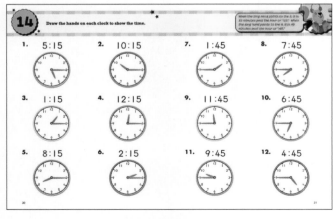

pages 30–31

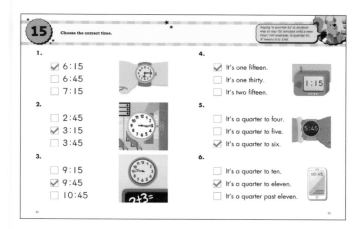

pages 32–33

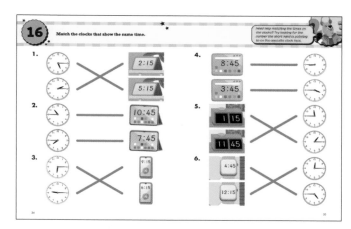

pages 34–35

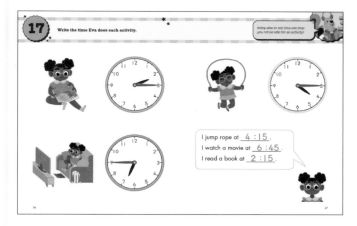

pages 36–37

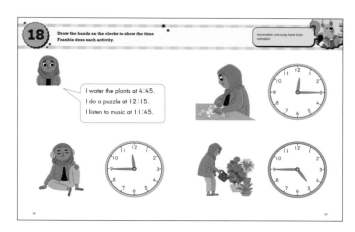

pages 38–39

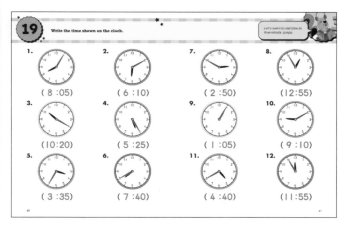

pages 40–41

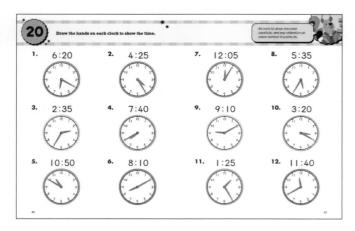

pages 42–43

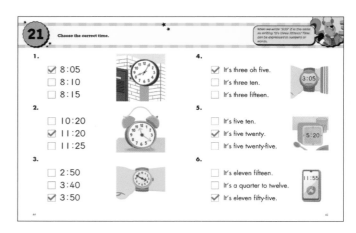

pages 44–45

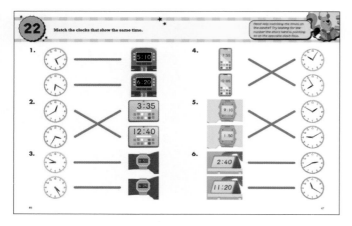

pages 46–47

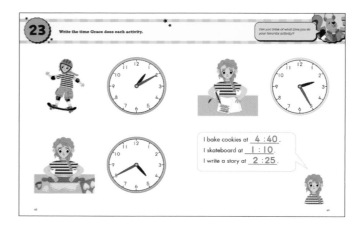

pages 48–49

pages 50–51

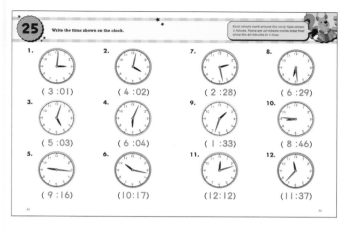

pages 52–53

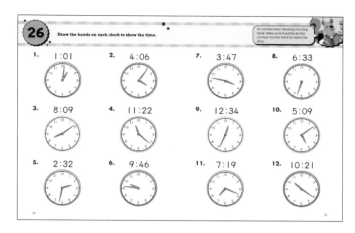

pages 54–55

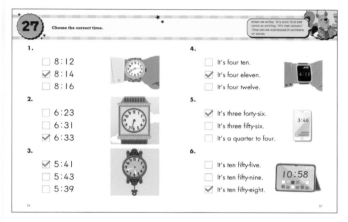

pages 56–57

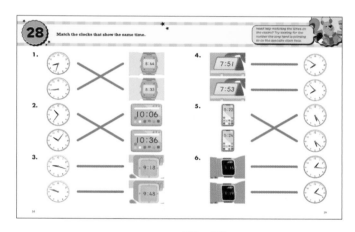

pages 58–59

pages 60–61

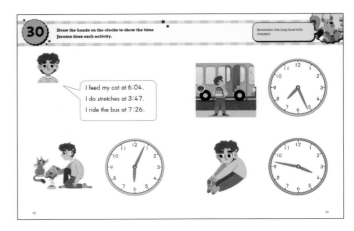

pages 62–63

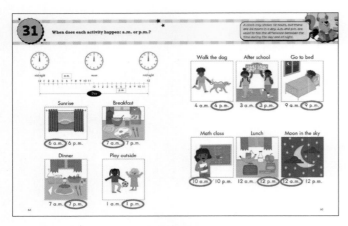

pages 64–65

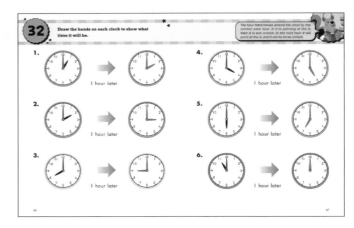

pages 66–67

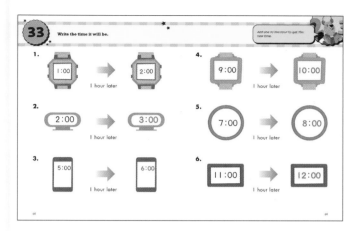

pages 68–69

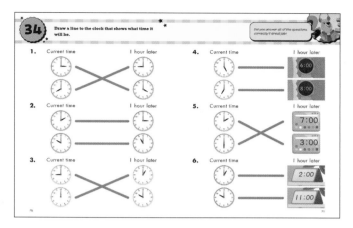

pages 70–71

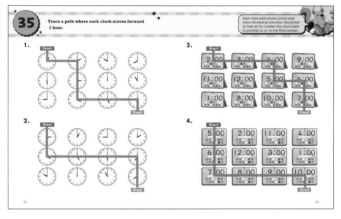

pages 72–73

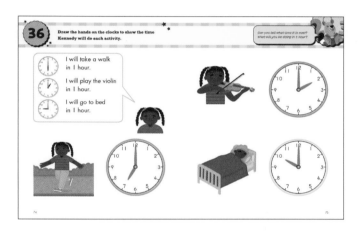

pages 74–75

123

pages 76–77

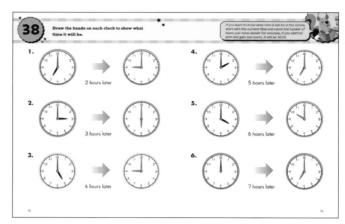

pages 78–79

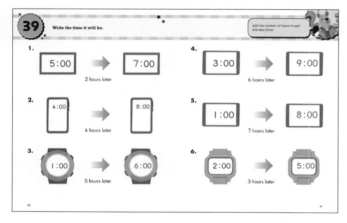

pages 80–81

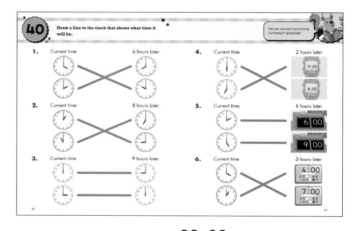

pages 82–83

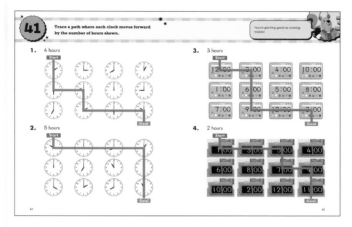

pages 84–85

pages 86–87

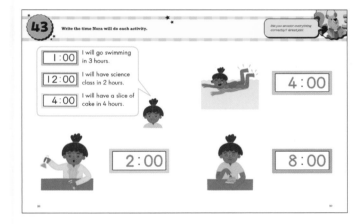

pages 88–89

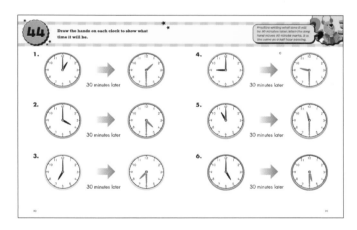

pages 90–91

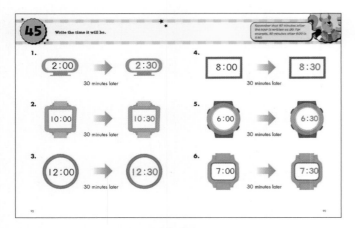

pages 92–93

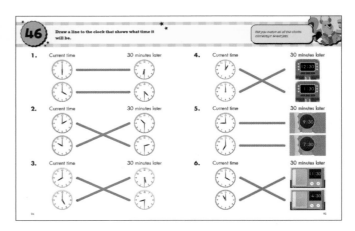

pages 94–95

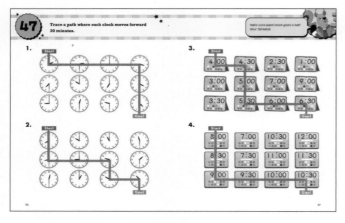

pages 96–97

pages 98–99

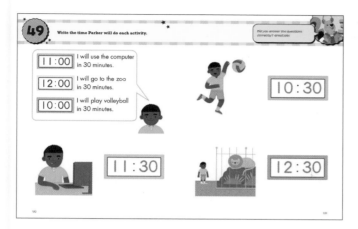

pages 100–101

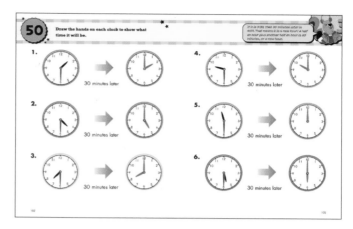

pages 102–103

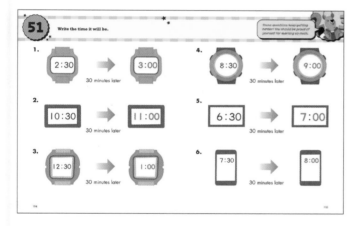

pages 104–105

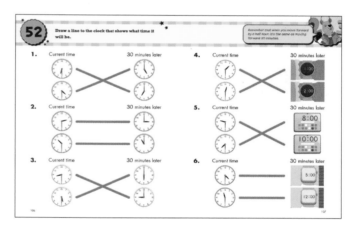

pages 106–107

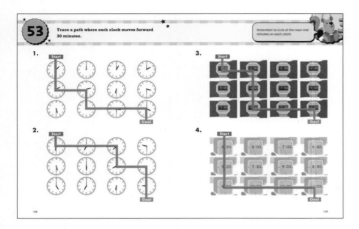

pages 108–109

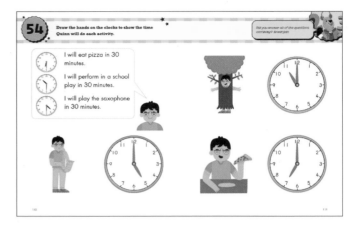

pages 110–111

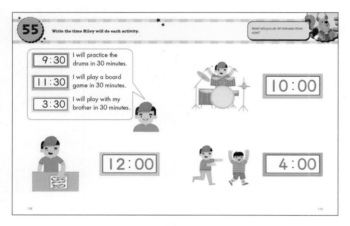

pages 112–113

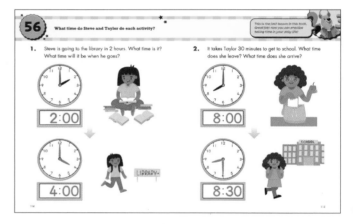

pages 114–115